First American Edition.
Copyright © 1998 Disney Enterprises, Inc.
All rights reserved under international copyright
conventions. Published in the United States by Grolier
Enterprises Inc., Danbury, Connecticut. Originally
published in Denmark by Egmont Gruppen, Copenhagen.

ISBN: 0-7172-8833-1

Manufactured in the United States of America.
A B C D   1 2 3 4

Long long ago, the Emperor of China ordered
that a great wall be built to protect his empire from
the evil Huns. In those days, a son brought honor
to his family by being a brave soldier. A daughter
brought honor to her family by being a good wife.

So it was that young women visited a Matchmaker
who would find them a husband. They had to impress
the Matchmaker.

One morning, a young woman named Mulan
was being prepared to visit the Matchmaker. Mulan
was nervous. She wasn't like other girls. She could
look proper, but could she *act* properly?

Mulan's mother placed a beautiful comb in her
daughter's hair.

"There, you're ready!" she said.

"Not quite!" Mulan's grandmother said.
"You'll need something for good luck."

Then she tied a small insect cage around
Mulan's waist.

"With this cricket, even you can't blow it!"

When Mulan finally met the Matchmaker, the visit did not go well. Poor Mulan was very nervous.

Then Mulan's lucky cricket escaped from its cage and landed on the Matchmaker's dress!

The Matchmaker was terrified. She fell back and landed against a lit stove. Suddenly her clothes caught fire!

"Put it out! Put it out!" the Matchmaker cried.

Mulan grabbed a teapot.

SPLASH!

"You are a disgrace!" the soaking wet Matchmaker shouted. "You may look like a bride, but you'll never bring your family honor."

Mulan returned home. When Fa Zhou saw his daughter's face, he guessed things had not gone well. While her horse Khan drank, Mulan wondered if she could ever bring honor to the family.

Mulan's father tried to cheer her up.

"What beautiful blossoms we have this year," he said.
He pointed to an unopened flower on a nearby tree.

"Look! This one is late, but I'll bet that when it
blooms, it will be the most beautiful of all."

Mulan smiled. Her father was saying that one day
she would bring honor to her family.

Just as Mulan
was starting to feel
better, she heard
the beating of a drum.
Mulan climbed the
wall and saw the
Emperor's advisor,
Chi Fu.

"The Huns have invaded China!" Chi Fu announced.
"By order of the Emperor, one man from every family
must serve in the Imperial Army!"

In his youth, Mulan's father had been a great soldier. But age and an old war wound had dulled his fighting ability. That evening, Mulan secretly watched him. Her heart filled with sadness. Mulan knew that he could not survive another battle, so she came up with a plan to save his life.

That night, Mulan quietly
sneaked into her parents'
bedroom. Carefully, she
took the scroll calling her
father to war. In its place,
she left her hair comb
as a token of her love.

Then Mulan took her father's sword
and cut her long, beautiful hair.
SLASH!

Mulan put <u>on</u> her father's combat uniform and left the house. She looked like a young soldier going to war. For this was her plan—to pretend to be a boy and take her father's place in the army.

As the rain poured down hard and cold, Mulan mounted her faithful horse, Khan.

She rode off, not knowing if she would ever see her family again.

Later that night, Mulan's parents discovered what she had done. They were shocked. Impersonating a soldier was a crime and if Mulan were caught, she would be killed. But there was nothing they could do. Mulan's grandmother prayed for help.

"Ancestors, hear our prayer," she pleaded. "Watch over Mulan."

Outside, in the garden temple, the Fa family's Ancestors heard the old woman's prayer.

The spirits agreed to send a Guardian to help Mulan. A little dragon named Mushu volunteered. Mushu had been demoted from his position as a family Guardian.

The Ancestors laughed at him.

The Ancestors had no faith in Mushu. So they ordered him to use his gong and awaken the most powerful Guardian of all—the Great Stone Dragon. Mushu approached the old statue.

"Yo, Rocky!" he called. "Wake up!"

The great dragon did not wake up. So Mushu climbed on to it and loudly banged the gong against its ear!

"Hello! Hellooo!" he yelled.

Suddenly, the dragon's ear broke off.

"Uh-oh," Mushu said.

The entire statue began to crack, and it crumbled to pieces!

"Oh, no, they're going to kill me!" said the panicky dragon.

Just then, Mushu saw Mulan's lucky cricket, Cri-Kee. Cri-Kee gave Mushu an idea. If Mushu could turn Mulan into a war hero, then the Ancestors would forgive him and make him a Guardian again.

So Mushu and Cri-Kee followed Mulan. But the little dragon was afraid that Mulan would not trust him. So, he cast a giant shadow of himself to make her think he was a big, wise and powerful dragon!

The tiny Mushu then stepped out from behind some rocks. "Who are you?" Mulan asked with surprise.

"Who am I? I am the powerful, the pleasurable, the indestructible Mushu!" he replied. "Pretty hot, huh?"

Mulan wasn't sure, but she did let him join her. She would need all the help she could get.

Later that day, Mulan reached the Imperial Army camp, where she met three recruits, Yao, Ling, and Chien-Po. Mulan tried to act like a man and slapped Yao on the back. But instead of starting a friendship, poor Mulan started a fight!

They stopped fighting when Captain Shang spoke. "Soldiers! Tomorrow, the real work begins."

The next day, combat training began. Shang fired an arrow into a tall pole and ordered Yao to get it. But first he tied two heavy bronze discs to Yao's wrists.

"One disc represents strength," Shang said. "The other represents discipline. You need both to reach the arrow."

Yao could not climb the pole. No one could.

In the days ahead, the recruits trained hard to be good soldiers.

Training was difficult for Mulan. Then, just when it seemed Mulan would never be a soldier, she realized how to climb the pole. Mulan tied the two discs together and used their weight to pull herself up the pole.

The soldiers cheered. Even Shang smiled!

All the training paid off. The recruits were now ready to fight.

Days later, they were marching through a
mountain pass. Suddenly, arrows began falling
from the sky. They were being attacked by
the Huns and their evil leader, Shan-Yu!

Shang ordered his men to fire the cannons.
BOOM! BOOM!

But the cannons were not enough. The Huns were winning.

"Aim the last cannon at Shan-Yu!" Shang cried desperately.

Just then, Mulan had an idea. She grabbed the last cannon and fired it. But instead of shooting at Shan-Yu, she aimed at the snow-covered mountain above him.

WHAM!

The cannon shell exploded into the mountain peak. Suddenly, the mountain began to rumble and snow started to fall. Mulan's plan worked. The noise started an avalanche! Shan-Yu saw what Mulan had done and tried to attack her, but he was too late. Soon, the Huns were completely buried in the snow.

Mulan was a hero. Although she had disobeyed Shang's order, she had saved the army and defeated the Huns.

"You are the craziest man I have ever met," Shang said to Mulan, "and for that I owe you my life. From now on you have my trust."

Mulan felt weak. She had been wounded by Shan-Yu. Suddenly, the young girl fainted!

Mulan was taken to the medic's tent, where the doctor discovered the truth—the brave soldier was a woman! Shang was shocked.

"I did it to save my father," Mulan explained.

Shang did not answer. Although Mulan was a hero, she had committed a terrible crime and must be punished.

Shang held Mulan's sword and prepared to strike,
but he could not, for Mulan had saved him. He
dropped the sword.

"A life for a life!" Shang said.

With that, Shang walked away and left Mulan
and Khan behind on the cold mountainside.

Mulan was very sad. She felt like a failure. Mushu tried to cheer her up.

"Come on, you've got to let these things go," he said. "You risked your life to help the people you love. At least you had good intentions."

Suddenly, Mulan saw Shan-Yu and five of his Huns. They were alive and heading for the Imperial City!

"We have to do something!" Mulan cried.

With that, she jumped up, grabbed her sword, and ran toward Khan. Mushu hesitated.

"Are we in this together or not?" Mulan asked the little dragon.

"Yeah!" Mushu agreed. "Let's go kick some Hunny buns!"

With Cri-Kee in tow, they rode off to the Imperial City.

Mulan arrived in the Imperial City
to find Shang and his men in a parade
celebrating the defeat of the Huns.

"Shang!" Mulan cried. "The Huns are alive.
They're in the city!"

"Why should I believe you?" Shang replied coldly.

Shang ignored Mulan. He rode off for the Imperial
Palace to meet the Emperor.

At the palace, Shang met the Emperor. Suddenly, one of the paper parade dragons ripped open. It was the Huns! They had hidden in the dragon so that they could attack the Emperor! The villains knocked Shang down, captured the Emperor and locked him inside the Palace.

Mulan rejoined her friends. To save the Emperor, they had to get inside. But how? Mulan had an idea. She, Yao, Ling and Chien-Po dressed like women to trick the Huns. With Shang, they climbed the Palace pillars.

Mulan, Yao, Ling and Chien-Po approached Shan-Yu's men...

…and quickly overpowered them!
Meanwhile, Shan-Yu was holding the Emperor captive.
"Bow to me!" he ordered.
But the Emperor bowed to no one!

Just in time, Shang burst in
and knocked down Shan-Yu.
As they fought, Chien-Po
grabbed the Emperor and
carried him to safety.

Shan-Yu knocked Shang out and chased Mulan onto the roof. He did not know that Mulan had planned a trap!

"Ready, Mushu?" Mulan cried.

"I am ready, baby!" Mushu answered.

With that, Mushu fired a rocket into Shan-Yu. The rocket took the villain away for ever!

Later, the Emperor presented Mulan with his own pendant and the sword of Shan-Yu.

"When they see this pendant, your family will know that you have saved the life of the Emperor," he said. "When they see this sword, the world will know that you have saved China."

Then the Emperor did the unthinkable—he bowed in respect to Mulan!

Mulan returned home. Her mother and grand-mother wept with joy and her father was filled with pride.

Soon, Mulan had an unexpected visitor. It was Shang. Mulan asked him to stay for dinner, and Shang happily accepted. Mulan's family watched the two with quiet contentment. They sensed a very special relationship was blooming.

As for Mushu, when the Ancestors learned of his deeds, they no longer laughed at the little dragon. They celebrated, and Mushu would officially become a family Guardian again. Mushu was thrilled.

"Send out for egg rolls!" he cried.